Floppy barked.

Floppy barked and barked.

"What is it?" said Biff.

Biff looked.

“What is it?” she said.

Wilf looked.

“What is it?” he said.

“What is it?” said Wilma.

“Is it a frog?”

“What is it?” said Chip.

"Is it a lizard?"

Mum looked at it.

"What is it?" said the children.

"It's a salamander," said Mum.

“It’s lost,” she said.

The salamander was safe.